Lipreading

Here is help and reassurance for anyone confronting hearing loss for the first time. At some point as we get older about a quarter of us ought to start using a hearing aid. But we won't get the best results from that alone and should combine it with lipreading. John Chaloner Woods was a firm advocate of lipreading classes, but for practice on our own with a mirror, with a friend or with the television, for those who can't get to classes or who want to experiment a little first, this guide to 'seeing the sound of speech' will be the greatest help.

It is organised around a series of photographs of the lipshapes illustrating those sounds that can be shown as static pictures. They can often provide the key to a whole word or sentence. John Chaloner Woods explains how they can be used and built on most effectively. From his own experience of learning lipreading, he warns us of the likely pitfalls. He also provides a wide variety of material that we can practise in front of our mirrors or that others can speak to us, helping us to gain familiarity and confidence in seeing speech.

John Chaloner Woods was a 'graduate' of the lipreading classes held by the Inner London Education Authority (ILEA) and the City Lit Centre for Deaf People, London. This booklet is based on his original text in *Lipreading – A Guide for Beginners*, first published by RNID in 1986.

Since I broke my glasses,
I've not been able to hear
so well.

Anon

Watch this face

A practical guide to lipreading

Based on an original text by John Chaloner Woods

Watch this face – A practical guide to lipreading

Based on the text of *Lipreading – A Guide for Beginners* by John Chaloner Woods

©The Estate of John Chaloner Woods 1986

First published by John Murray (Publishers) Ltd in 1986
Reissued in 1991
Second edition 1994
Revised edition 2001 under new title: *Watch this face –
A practical guide to lipreading*
Revised edition 2003

RNID
19-23 Featherstone Street
London EC1Y 8SL

British Library Cataloguing-in-Publication Data
A catalogue record for this book is available from the
British Library

ISBN 0 900634 99 5

Contents

Introduction   **1**

Chapter 1   **Seeing the sound of speech**   **7**

Lipreading classes   **7**

Hearing aids   **11**

Approaches to lipreading   **12**

Anticipation and context   **14**

How long does it take to learn?   **15**

Using the photographs   **16**

Learning outside a class   **17**

Phrases with the same rhythm   **17**

Party tricks   **18**

Tips for family and friends   **20**

Chapter 2   **Starting with the mirror**   **23**

Chapter 3   **P B M**   **27**

Chapter 4   **F V PH**   **33**

Chapter 5   **The long vowels – AH, AW, OO, EE, ER – and the importance of stress**   **37**

Chapter 6   **SH**   **47**

Chapter 7   **TH and the invisibles – T, D, N, hard G, hard C, hard K**   **51**

Contents

Chapter 8   L and dark L   57

Chapter 9   R and combinations   61

Chapter 10   W and Q   65

Chapter 11   S, X and Z   69

Chapter 12   Double vowels   71

Chapter 13   Short vowels, neutral vowels
             and accents   75

Chapter 14   Speaking without voice   81

Chapter 15   Final thoughts   87

Appendix 1
             Lipspeaking   91

Appendix 2
             Hearing aids   95
             Ear wax   96

Appendix 3
             Loops and infrared systems   97

Publications   101

Useful addresses   103

About RNID and ATLA   105

Introduction

Like many other people, hearing loss has come as I have grown older. Many of us have difficulty with the high-pitched sounds. We may be able to hear the vowels which have more energy than the high frequencies. The high frequencies have little energy and are lost with age. Bats flying in the dark make a sound of such high frequency that only dogs and children up to the age of seven are capable of hearing it. The bats use it as a sort of radar to locate the position of objects ahead. Adults are most unlikely to hear it, showing that a small degree of hearing loss occurs early in life. The eardrum comprises a small piece of skin capable of vibrating in accordance with the frequencies of the sound reaching it. Presumably the more perfect the elasticity of the drum, the greater the volume of sounds receivable.

To hear we must listen

For years we can go to the theatre, to meetings, have discussions, listen to the radio and television and still hear everything perfectly well. Then gradually, people who will not speak up, or who mumble, seem to have increased since we were young. They do not seem to teach children in schools to speak properly.

Even many politicians and public speakers seem never to have learned elocution. Members of the public interviewed on television or radio often speak so badly that it is a waste of time to listen. We all know that to hear we must listen, but it all gets very frustrating. This is what happened to me.

Eventually I became quite skilled at placing my hand precisely in a cup shape at an exact distance from my ear, thereby improving the power to listen. Of course, other people noticed what I was doing and dropped hints that my ears might need a visit to the doctor's for syringing, when I could hear perfectly well in the ordinary way. At last I gave in and went to an Ear, Nose and Throat specialist near Harley Street. He suctioned the wax out of my ear canal, instead of syringing. After the second visit I went, cheque-book in hand, to his secretary and asked, 'How much?' What she replied sounded alarmingly like 'Fifty', so I put my hand to my ear with a querulous expression and she said, 'Fifteen pounds'.

You can guess the next thing: I went to my doctor and he gave me a letter to the consultant at the hospital. He carried out a hearing test and prescribed a hearing aid, which I received some time after – all free.

A photographer by trade, I had a little pendulum in my darkroom. It made a tick every second by which I timed the exposure when making prints. It was becoming difficult to hear. I found I could see a shadow cast by the pendulum from the safe-light and I carried on until I realised it had lost its tick altogether. I examined it and could find no explanation. There was not really anything to go wrong. The day I got my hearing aid, I went into the darkroom and just gave the pendulum a push. It ticked loud and clear!

Age-related hearing loss affects the high frequency range of sounds more than the lower frequencies. The hearing aid attempts to increase the volume of the high frequencies more than the volume of the lower ones. This produces a distortion, to balance the distortion created by the hearing

Use a mirror to increase your confidence in seeing speech.

loss. In good conditions this works pretty well and makes it possible to hear words you would otherwise not be able to hear. However, there are many occasions when a hearing aid alone is unable to help and that is when lipreading plays a very important role.

Soon after birth people born with sight and hearing begin to attach meaning to a friendly face or an angry word. Babies learn by direct aural and visual observance and imitation of what is seen and heard. The signals sent by the nerves of the ears and eyes are translated by the brain into sounds and sight. The brain develops and adds to its store of information with the growth of the child into an adult. But during a working life, some instinctive learning skills are forgotten.

Unused skill

I have a strong memory of what I felt at my first lipreading class where the teacher switched off her voice. Since then I have observed how newcomers respond when they join. This leaves me with little doubt that a long-unused skill is aroused, as meaning is found from this strange experience. When hearing was unimpaired there was no need to notice what speech looked like – it was audible and required no conscious attention to its appearance. At the first session when speech is deliberately silent, the neglected skill begins to return: we see words, a phrase, or perhaps a simple sentence. We see the sound of speech. Practice in this new use of our eyes gradually builds a visual vocabulary.

Progress will be more rapid if you can go to a lipreading class. However, with the diligent use of a mirror, or with a friend, or with the television, and practice in speaking without voice, you can successfully learn to see speech. The word most commonly used in this country for the skill needed to learn to see speech is 'lipreading' and classes will generally be called 'lipreading classes'. Sadly, many older people with a common form of hearing loss may be put off the idea because it sounds like learning another language. Actually it is learning to see a language already known and comes naturally by practice, leading out of unused memory from past experience.

Visibility of speech

Tests have been made choosing two groups of people: one group comprising those with hearing and no experience of lipreading, the other of people with a hearing loss and practice in lipreading. Single words were spoken without voice to each member of each group. The surprising result was the degree of success scored by the group with no experience of lipreading. This shows that hearing people probably all have some residual sense of visibility of speech.

The adventure of learning to see speech is not at all like entering a dark tunnel. Signposts are soon found to encourage further exploration. The photographs in this book are signposts pointing to the visibility of certain speech sounds. They represent those sounds that can be shown as static shapes, but you must remember that they are always seen in movement during speech. The deliberate and accurate formation of these shapes during speech helps visibility and therefore understanding. They often provide the key to a whole word or sentence.

Practice in speaking without voice is important not only to those who want to communicate with deaf and hard of hearing people, but also to the deaf people themselves when learning to see voiceless speech. Both should feel that the voiceless speech is well formed. Respect for these signposts will help conversation, preventing exaggerated mouthing or careless pronunciation.

Chapter 1

Seeing the sound of speech

Lipreading classes

When I went to the hearing aid centre and was having an impression of my ear made, I asked the lady doing it about lipreading. On hearing the word she suddenly became enthusiastic and said, "I'll get you details. We have a class at the hospital. I'll find the day and time of the next class." I had only a vague idea of what lipreading was. In the back of my mind was the thought that my hearing loss, although mild, might be progressive and that my hearing aid might need supplementing.

So I turned up at the appropriate time, wondering if I would be accepted and what a lipreading class would be like – a bit like my first day at school. I was welcomed and given a most interesting introduction to the subject by practising lipreading speech without voice. I met people who regarded any degree of hearing loss as a simple matter of fact, rather like a game of cards. Some get a good hand, some a bad one, but whatever you have been dealt, that is the hand you must play and you might as well enjoy the game.

With a comparatively mild loss, you feel a bit of a fraud because you can hear many things perfectly well. You should not worry on that account. An important advantage of a lipreading class is that you meet others with a hearing loss

At noisy parties, stand near someone you know well and can lipread.

and you no longer feel uniquely different. It is also a good thing to meet people who speak quite naturally about their own deafness. One said to me, "Mine started while I was still at primary school." I realised that was why he was difficult to understand because he could not hear his own voice very well. Another could speak, but was profoundly deaf. His hearing had been destroyed by disease at a later stage, so he knew what speech sounded like and had learned to control his own voice, although he could not hear it. He carried on a conversation with the teacher, lipreading what she said and speaking what he had to say.

There are classes throughout the country – more in some areas than in others. I regard myself as extremely lucky for two reasons. Firstly, because I went straight to a class from the hearing aid centre. Secondly, because I never thought that I was, at my age, embarking upon the acquisition of a new skill. If I had stopped to think, I might never have started. Now I have no regrets and I can face the years ahead with a moderate skill. There are innumerable occasions when, with a combination of a hearing aid, lipreading and my residual hearing, I can get the message – in shops, at meetings, in conversations, and of course with the television. In conditions with excessive background noise, such as a crowded room with everyone talking, (or shouting), the hearing aid amplifies *all* the noise, not what you want to hear.* Only lipreading and experience can overcome these conditions.

Lipreading classes are usually run by your local authority's Adult Education Service. Your local library, education department or the Association of Teachers of Lipreading to Adults (ATLA) should have details (see Useful addresses on page 103).

Although there are only two million hearing aid users in the UK, there are a further three million people who could benefit from them. It is surprising therefore that more people do not attend lipreading classes, as so much information can be found there. My experience tells me that a hearing aid solves many problems, but leaves many unsolved. It may well be that, with the older population, classes on a rehabilitative theme offering perhaps six introductory sessions in the first place would be more suitable for people who are starting to lose their hearing. These could cover how a hearing aid works, or doesn't; what to do about it; when not to wear it; what it can realistically be expected to do. Then a lesson on sound, its quirks, what happens to it when passed through

*This may not be the case with digital hearing aids.

another device, like a hearing aid or telephone. This could be followed by one on our alphabet, for example sounds made by letters are different from the names of the letters. Then something about the language, its richness and peculiarities: how hearing people communicate and what hearing loss implies and what changes in the situation there might be.*

There may be variations across the country about charging a fee for classes, but for pensioners and disabled people it is likely to be moderate or nominal. Complications can arise if the class you choose is organised by an authority other than the one in whose area you live. If you have doubts about committing yourself to one period a week during school term time, you should see the teacher, and also find out whether other subjects relating to listening and hearing are dealt with.

Members of a class, of course, come from all sorts of occupations. Very often, introductions are made using Christian names: the qualification for membership is hearing loss. A pleasant atmosphere in the class comes from the keenness and concentration of everyone – teacher and students. After about an hour it is usual to have a coffee break. At that point everyone often starts talking at once. If you have discovered that you cannot get on with your hearing aid in a room full of people,

*Lipreading teachers are now encouraged to offer short courses, as John Chaloner Woods suggested. Hearing therapists also provide this service.

now is your chance to find out how to cope.

A doctor psychologist once told me, "Weigh up the pros and cons and give the most careful thought to matters which are not really important but, with the really important ones, act upon a hunch." I am convinced that anyone who has worked alone, or with a friend or friends, on the exercises suggested in this book is now up against a decision upon a really important matter.

If lipreading is making you tired, have forty winks in your chair or go to bed.

So do not think for too long about a lipreading class. If you can find one, join it! I have noticed on occasion that when there is something popular on the television numbers in the class drop. There was once – I think it was the last class in the term – when I and the teacher were the class. So I had a session of private tuition which I think interested both of us, and encouraged me.

Hearing aids

The danger of relying entirely upon a hearing aid is that you might slide back into the state of isolation which drove you to the hearing aid centre in the first place. A hearing aid can be a trap, insofar as it does not solve all hearing problems. It is a truism to say that to hear we must listen. Once hearing loss occurs, we must listen with our eyes as well as our ears. It takes a positive effort. Not listening is a negative and a dangerous habit. If you can read a book or a paper all evening while the radio and television are on in the same room, you are acquiring a skill which is the opposite of what you want from hearing. Be careful. If you are tired, it would be better to have forty winks in your chair or go to bed.

The best way to look at it is that both the hearing aid and lipreading are adjuncts to listening, not a substitute for hearing, at least for those who have any useful hearing left. (For more on hearing aids see Appendix 2 on page 95.)

Approaches to lipreading
There are two mental approaches to lipreading – the analytic and the synthetic or rhythmic. The analytic seems primarily to read each sound accurately and translate the whole into the language correctly. The synthetic seeks to observe the flow or rhythm of the language, getting the meaning or sense of the message with the help of intuition and any visual clues, foresight and hindsight, and not interrupting the flow by too much analytical precision. There is a good case for both methods: the analytic in the early stages and a combination of both methods when the skills have advanced enough. Nobody knows exactly what goes on in the brain when we learn to 'see'

sounds by lipreading, nor does a teacher know how students learn. Probably those whose approach is more analytic will find the synthetic method too vague and the synthetic learners will tend to find analytic drill too boring, so a bit of each is used. I have been persuaded not to use the word 'invisible' in relation to the sounds most difficult to see, because there may always be someone who can see some little movement of a muscle somewhere. Sheer mental agility, in spite of there being no obvious context or clue, may provide the solution.

Memory
A lively memory and knowledge of the subject is a great help in lipreading and should be developed, although some of us whose hearing loss is due to age may feel that youth has the advantage of us! As the 'oldest inhabitant' in my class, I sometimes wonder to what extent you can teach an old dog new tricks. In my younger days I heard the expression 'second childhood' applied to other people and I thought I understood it. Now, particularly when I have just made a stupid mistake, I begin to wonder. Childhood is a time when the capacity to learn is at its highest.

Anticipation and context

Lipreading practice with qualified teachers is usually without voice because this concentrates the attention on seeing. Anticipation, mental alertness and alacrity are encouraged to help the lipreader. It is much easier to lipread the words you are expecting. I remember in a very early class when I was thinking ahead and was sure a certain word was bound to come, but – you know the way it is – I forgot the word, my mind went blank. Sure enough the word came and I lipread it! It was the strangest feeling. The word lost in my mind reappeared by lipreading.

The most difficult exercise in lipreading is when there is no context. When there is some clue as to the subject, the difficulty is reduced. For example, at the breakfast table, if someone asks you, 'Please pass the marmalade', this is very much easier to lipread than some comment about the foreign news, especially if you haven't yet seen the paper. Therefore, if you want a person to lipread what you have to say, start by providing a context or clue, if one does not already exist. In a lot of everyday situations we all get the message, whether we hear the words or not, if we see the speaker's face and gesture. 'How are you?' 'What a beautiful day.' 'Can't stop now, must catch this bus.' Or (yawn) 'I'm off to bed now.' There is little difficulty in getting the message, with or without hearing or lipreading. The context of the occasion helps the lipreader to anticipate what may be coming. 'I saw a conjurer saw a girl in half.' The context makes it easy to recognise the same sound (saw) as being two distinct words with different meanings, as we already do, reading it in print or hearing it.

Sound, not spelling

Lipreading is concerned with sounds, not spelling. As a baby and toddler you learnt the sound, meaning and appearance of speech, before learning the alphabet. Now, you must think only of sound, meaning, and what it looks like on the face, but not spelt out on the page. The context sorts out words making the same sound. 'Bow' may mean the bough of a tree, the bow of a boat or a bending of the body. The problem is not new to lipreading. What is new to lipreading is the context having to sort out words which may sound different but look the same because they make the same lip movement. For instance, the word 'pop' and 'bomb'.

How long does it take to learn?

A number of factors are involved – age, memory, aptitude, degree of hearing loss, the urgency of the desire to learn. The milder the degree of hearing loss, the longer it may take to learn because a hearing aid is enough to help in many situations. The greater the degree of hearing loss, the more urgent it becomes to remember to practise whenever possible.

Lipreading requires great concentration. Don't forget to take a break after about an hour.

The goal for most of us will be to combine hearing and lipreading, but it is necessary to acquire enough skill at lipreading without voice. If you want an idea of how long it takes to become a real expert lipreader, I know of someone struck by total deafness through an illness. It was just as he had qualified for a good career, but the deafness meant he had to abandon it. Sheer character and courage, working hard with six lessons a week with various teachers for five years, an expert lipreader was created, able to work in another branch of the same profession in which he had originally qualified.

Using the photographs

The photographs can be used on your own or with a mirror. They help you judge the effect on your own face, getting the feel of each lipshape, practising the whole words and short phrases as well, seeing movement from shape to shape. Undoubtedly, this could teach one to speak more clearly and would serve as an introduction to lipreading.

Learning outside a class

If you are unable to find a class near to where you live, it would be ideal to find someone, or a small group, who are willing to attend regular sessions to practise lipreading and speaking without voice. Probably an hour is a long enough session for the intense concentration required for lipreading without voice, or even half an hour. Qualified teachers of lipreading go to a great deal of trouble to make what is to be lipread interesting and relevant to the lipshapes being studied. It is a good idea if two or more friends arrange to have practice sessions together to decide at the beginning who is going to speak without voice and who is to be the lipreader. This could mean taking turns, but it also clarifies who, as the one with their voice switched off, must prepare the subject for each occasion. This in itself becomes part of the learning process, because you need to consider what is easy to lipread and what is difficult or nearly impossible.

Phrases with the same rhythm

When the person who has switched off their voice is preparing for a session, homophonous words like 'bough' and 'bow' (which sound and look the same on the lips) are not so much a problem, because the context distinguishes them. The real problem comes with phrases which have the same rhythm.

'It distresses me when my daughters argue.'
'It distresses me when my corsets are new.'

Try those words on the lips of your image in the mirror. (The real expert lipreader might spot the difference between 'daughters' and 'corsets' and 'argue' and 'are new'.) Then try the whole sentences. Have a look at the photographs. Each of them is a basic lipshape you need to make properly to produce the particular sound which occurs in speech. The 'au' and 'or' sounds in 'daughters' and 'corsets' is the long vowel 'aw' (page 37). The 'ar' in 'argue' is the same as in 'are' – the long vowel 'ah' (page 37). The 'ue' in 'argue' is the same as in 'new' – the double vowel – 'ewe' or 'u'.

The rhythm of the two phrases is very much the same, and the lipreader might well be pleased if either phrase had been read correctly. If not, the result could be some hilarious laughter, a welcome relief from the concentration needed for lipreading. Context would make one or other of the phrases nonsense, and so simplify things.

Party tricks
If there are any occasions when it would be wise to hide your hearing difficulty, they are few indeed. Admitting hearing loss generally produces a very favourable response with most hearing people. It is also an opportunity to inform others of

how they can help you. Ask them to talk directly to you, slightly slower than usual. They are very happy when they are successful in helping you to understand what they are saying. So don't try to hide your hearing aid. People often notice it and speak a little louder and more clearly.

As far as possible take a positive attitude to your hearing loss and avoid 'opting out', lest it become a habit. Even parties with lots of people talking at the top of their voices should be experienced. You can invent a technique for having a conversation with a friend in such conditions. You have to get very close, with your hearing aid well positioned (or even switched off), so that you can see your friend speaking. It is well worth experimenting. But you may be forgiven if you find you 'opt out' by being engaged for the next party. You could also ask a friend to prompt you as to the subject of the conversation. Stand near someone you know well and can lipread.

I will let you into a secret I have discovered. Some lipreaders have found a way to cope with such situations. Lipreading is always rather hard work and can be avoided by keeping talking yourself as long as you can hold a person's interest, then sliding away with the friendliest of smiles.

You need to see a speaker's whole face when lipreading.

Tips for family and friends

Family and friends are a problem when you start lipreading. Not everyone takes kindly to hints that exaggerated mouthing of words may be more difficult to lipread than careful speech, pronouncing every syllable, and that anything like a shout is more difficult too. It is like those people who think it helps to shout down the phone when calling America or who make themselves understood by shouting slowly in English at French waiters.

Hand in front of mouth.

Constant movement of head.

Looking the other way.

These are among the things to encourage your friends to avoid.

Long ago, before I had any reason to think about hearing, I devised a way to speak to my father after he developed a hearing loss. I would say the first few words in an ordinary voice. When he showed any sign of attention I would repeat the words in much the same voice and he would generally hear. My mother used to say, "He can hear when he wants to." I know now that after I had got his attention, he then heard me speak, saw my face and probably used lipreading.

A good way to train family and friends who need to communicate vocally is to get a discussion going on the lipshapes illustrated here – as to whether they are exaggerated or not. Keep the discussion going as long as they will play. It may develop into an argument, because colloquial speech is often too rapid for the shapes to be formed properly. To draw out the opinions of the people who switch off their voice, lipreaders and those who just talk, is a tactful way to avoiding too many 'do's and don'ts', which are liable to be resented. One thing that this should teach is that a lipreader takes longer to interpret the shapes seen than a hearing person takes to recognise sounds, at least until the lipreader becomes more expert than I and many others have become.

Body language
There has been much written about the unspoken 'body language' that we all use, consciously and unconsciously, to supplement what we are saying – facial expressions, gestures, positions of arms and legs. Lipreading is, if you like, the most sophisticated body language of all. Research has proved that hearing people lipread individual test words (without voice) as well as deaf people. This indicates that we all lipread to some extent. People who live in cities in particular need to watch a companion on the tube or in a crowded restaurant. It is a question of building on this.

Our eyes have to build a skill upon not-too-well-observed, fleeting shapes upon the speaker's face. It is a marvel really that the brain is capable of doing it. When I mentioned lipreading to a friend, who I could see had difficulty with hearing, he said, "I have not got the type of brain which would adapt to such a process." A better attitude to the problem would be that of the man who, when asked if he could play the violin, answered, "I don't know, I've never tried." So if you don't know whether you can lipread, this book should give you a chance to try.

I have often thought that I have learned a certain word after failing to recognise it many times, when at last I have spotted it successfully. After a little time there may always be another failure with the same word. I am writing of lipreading without voice. If one can ignore failures and remember successes, the balance gradually moves towards success. Remembering the difficulty, success is its own reward, well-earned and highly valued on any occasion, even if it is only one sentence that one has captured.

Chapter 2

Starting with the mirror

If you have bought this book and haven't been to a lipreading class, have no one at the moment with whom you can practise lipshapes, or feel shy about it, then this is when the mirror comes in. Say 'peacock' with and without voice, watching your image in the mirror. When you say 'pea' the lips part, showing a wide opening for the 'ee' sound. The 'c' and 'ck' of 'cock' are not usually visible but the syllable 'cock' appears as a slight movement of the jaw. Incidentally, 'peacock' is a good example of a word where seeing and hearing dovetail in for the benefit of lipreaders with some hearing. The 'pea' is easy to see while the 'cock' is difficult to see but quite easy to hear. There are plenty of others.

It is quite a job to arrange to work with a mirror. So to save all the trouble of setting it up in a good light and a quiet private place, it will be worthwhile arranging somewhere easy to work in at any time. Don't work too hard with the mirror but have a rest and a change by watching television or having a chat with someone. Then try to remember to watch for lipshapes when there is a reasonable close-up of someone talking on the television. Not to worry if you become interested and forget to watch. Using a mirror is quite hard work. Remember that this is a less than ideal way to introduce lipreading and speaking without voice. See if you can start to get into a habit of watching people's faces when

When there is a close-up of someone on television, look at their lipshapes.

they speak, rather than just their lips. Experiment with switching off your hearing aid, or taking if off, or not putting it on. (Warning: without your hearing aid there is a risk outdoors where there is traffic.) Lipreading and speaking without voice is a live method of communication. Reading about it is an intellectual exercise which could become rather deadly. So if you feel a bit bored with it as you read, let your mind wander in a search for somebody who might share a live interest, as a substitute for a teacher and a class. If you could get a real person, instead of your own image in the mirror, to speak the things I suggest, you would be getting real practice. But do not stop using the mirror. Let your friends use it too.

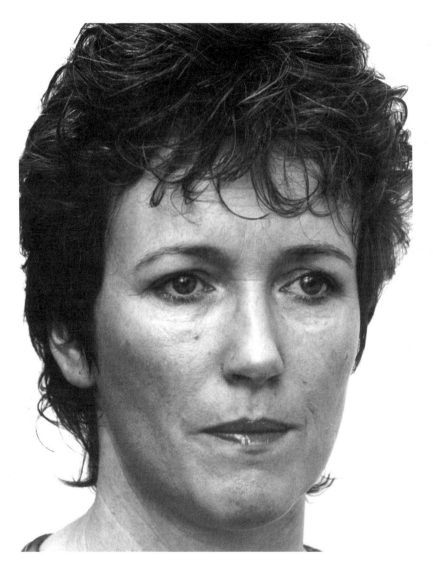

Pea   **Bunch**   **Marmalade**

Chapter 3

P B M

So let us start with the lipshape P, B, M (see photograph). This
shape appears the same for each sound. It is also one of the
easiest to recognise. The words 'pea', 'bee', 'me' spoken without
voice, separately, alone and without any clue or context, are
visually indistinguishable. Given a context, this is no problem.

'A bunch of sweet peas.'

'A swarm of bees.'

'Who? Me?'

Incidentally, did you notice that a 'bunch of sweet peas' has
the P, B, M shape twice? And then you say, 'Who? Me?' and
your expression changes. This is all part of lipreading and
professional lipspeaking. Lipreading requires concentration –
you cannot take your eyes off the speaker's face for one
moment – and observation trained by practice and more
practice. Professionally trained lipspeakers are required to
study the techniques of speech and empathise with the
lipreader (see Appendix 1 on page 91).

Facial expression and gestures help to convey meaning.

Watch and listen
I have chosen the P, B, M lipshapes to show what you are in for. Over and over again I have failed to read a voiceless sentence in class because I thought a word included the sound M when it was in fact a P or B. With the M sound I could not make sense, but my brain obstinately refused to try P or B which would have given me the word. What a joy it is now to hear and lipread together and never be caught by the P, B, M shape. It is easily seen and heard. The reason for this is that, for hearing people, M is a nasal sound, and as such is easily distinguished by ear. B is distinguished from P because of its voice quality. Listening practice will show those with some hearing that many lipreading problems will fade when they are watching and listening.

I think that with voiceless lipreading it is sometimes just possible to detect M as very slightly different from the other two, but it is difficult to be sure that there has not been a context clue.

Here are suggestions for mirror practice:

'Being a Member of Parliament makes him an MP.'

'Perhaps he'll become Prime Minister.'

Note how you say MP and Prime Minister, and some other words like 'empire' and 'import'. The M and P come together – the visual result is the closing of the lips once, not twice.

'His performance prevented a bitter battle being fought between the opposition and the Government.'

'Better employment becomes a primary purpose.'

'Many believe it all began with a great big bang.'

Another suggestion for practice is to watch a speaker on television and count the number of times you see the P, B, M form on the speaker's face.

Then, to keep up interest, count the F shapes only, or SH, TH, or L shapes only. Such exercises are basic eye training which, when combined with some voiceless training, will later enable you to get the most out of lipreading combined with your hearing aid.

Watch speakers on the TV and count how many times they make a particular lipshape.

In a class a qualified teacher might spend three sessions on the P, B, M lipshape, taking each one at a time. Many other lipshapes will also come into sentences and gradually familiarity with others will be introduced. The limitations of the printed word mean that you are thrown on to your own devices to get some practice with the mirror. Invent little phrases to speak clearly to your image without using your voice.

'A penny for your thoughts.'

You can observe the P and three long vowel sounds – AW (the same sound), the second starting with Y, which is not very visible, the third with TH. Say, 'for your thoughts'. Perhaps you can see the Y, perhaps not. You can exaggerate the Y a little to make it more visible.

'Perhaps we should buy a mini.'

Just observe what you can (or cannot – like the H) see – two Ps, an S, a W, EE again, SH (a good one to see), a B and an M.

'Peter Piper picked a peck of pickled pepper.'

'Many a slip 'twixt cup and lip.'

There is an L twice, a W again, an X to compare with an S.

'Sing a song of sixpence.'

A CE to compare with S. That's why only the sound matters in lipreading – not the spelling. Consider these:

bough	**bow**
cough	**cof**
fight	**fite**
height	**hite**
laugh	**lahf**
rough	**ruf**
thorough	**thuhra**
though	**tho**
thought	**thawt**
through	**throo**

Be thankful you are learning to lipread and are not a foreigner trying to learn English or a child learning to spell!

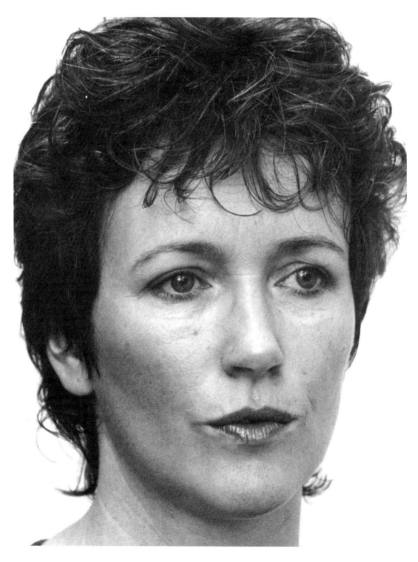

Fun   **Fifty-five**   **Photograph**

Chapter 4

F V PH

Visually, these sounds are identical in appearance and easy
to see, but the V has a different audible sound, and that
difference can be important. The correct lipshape is the lower
lip coming up to the upper front teeth.

'Few looked at the view.'

Sight alone cannot distinguish between the first and last
words 'few' and 'view', but there is an audible difference
which you may be able to detect with a hearing aid.

'Very few photographed the view.'

When watching speech without voice, words beginning with a
V often cause difficulty because the F or PH is more common,
and V is unexpected. The solution, with experience, is to try
the effect of substituting a V for an F and getting the sense.

'Full of flowers' is an example of one word ending with F and the
next word beginning with F. Normal speech produces one
slightly prolonged F. 'Fifty-five' is a number you should read
accurately, but 'fifteen' or 'fifty' are numbers easily misread. All '-
teens' and '-tys' are danger signals for lipreading. We are taught
always to check when these occur. The way to do this is to ask
the question. 'Did you say fifteen?' and the answer should be
'Yes' or 'No', so telling you which it was. You must not ask, 'Did

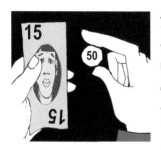

Numbers are easily misread. Watch out for the '-teens' and '-tys'.

you say fifty or fifteen?' because the answer you will get will leave you in as much doubt as you were in before. 'Yes' or 'No' should be quite clear, at least if you can see the speaker's face.

Mental alacrity is needed again to avoid selecting the wrong lipshape out of the three, F, V or PH – finish, television and telephone. Say this to the mirror:

'Father fought for his fee for providing further food.'

It is rather a silly sentence, but it contains several Fs and also the set of long vowels which occur in lipreading (see page 37). Notice that the words 'fought', 'for' and 'four' have the same vowel shape and sound regardless of spelling. Practise in the mirror with these words and watch the difference between the F shape and the P, B, M shape. Also notice that GH joins F, V, PH in looks and sound on these occasions.

fun   **pun**

bun   **mum**

muff   **tough**

trough   **fool**

pool   **mule**

AH

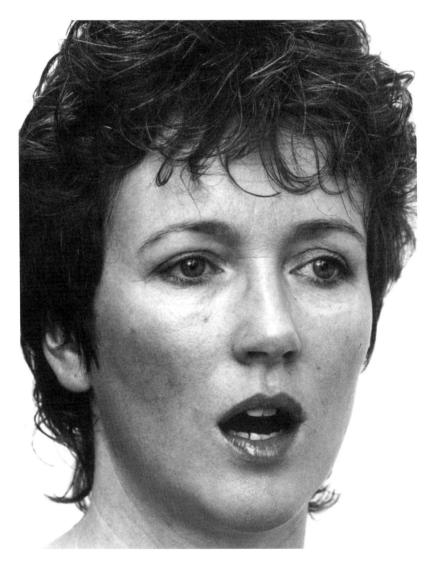

Car **Laugh** **Part**

Chapter 5

The long vowels – AH, AW, OO, EE, ER – and the importance of stress

A, E, I, O, U, the vowels of the alphabet that you learnt in school, have little to do with the vowels seen and heard in speech. So let's concentrate on what we can see. You must work with the signpost photographs and the mirror in front of you.

Say AH: the vowel in 'car', 'heart', 'laugh', 'part', 'rasp', 'tart', 'half'. Watching your face in the mirror, you will see that the AH sound is made by dropping the jaw to open the mouth (voiceless) – just what a baby does as a spoonful of food approaches.

Say AW: the same movement as AH except the corners of the mouth move inwards and lips forward as the mouth opens, and the jaw may jut forward a bit. 'Awful', 'bought', 'caught', 'fort', 'George', 'jaw', 'law', 'lord', 'more', 'roar', 'tort', 'taught', 'wart', ('your', as sometimes pronounced).

Say OO: the jaw comes up and makes the OO sound. 'Who', 'coup', 'ghoul', 'loot', 'two', 'rue', 'truce'. Words like 'new', 'few', are subtly different – they are double vowels (see page 71). They look familiar but not quite the same to the sharp eye.

EE is a clear vowel to see, if properly spoken. The corners of the mouth are widened, almost a smile. It is a wide, narrow,

horizontal shape. A lot depends upon the face of the speaker, whether the movement shows teeth naturally or not. It is possible to make the EE sound more visible, but don't overdo it. Practise in the mirror – watch other people. Say to the mirror 'it's easy' –

Always remember to face someone who is lipreading you.

the I is a short vowel (see page 75) and the EA is the long vowel EE. There is not much difference to see, but plenty to hear.

Finally there is a long vowel **ER**. Say 'bird', 'curd', 'dirty', 'flirt', 'hurt', 'jerk', 'learn', 'mirth', 'purpose', 'sir', 'turf', 'verb', 'word', 'earn', 'urn'. The corners of the mouth come inwards, the jaw drops slightly and the lower lip moves forward.

Seeing speech

The aim of practice is to work towards instant recognition by sight of these long vowels as confirmation of what you hear. (I can hear when I can see.) I have often found it a great encouragement when the television newsreader disappears, and is replaced by a map, but goes on talking. I lose what she is saying until she returns to the screen again, but then I can see and hear once more. The time spent on these long vowels will not be wasted.

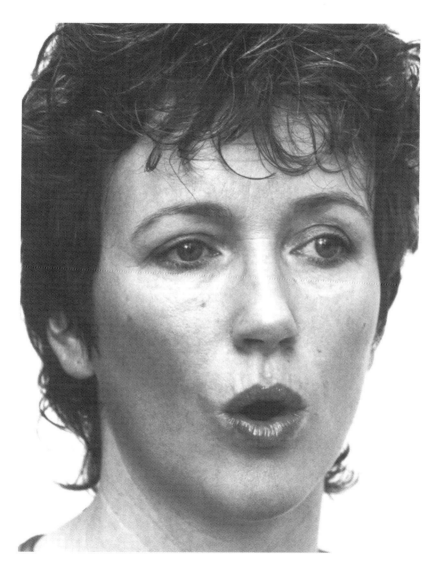

Awful   **Fought**   **More**

oo

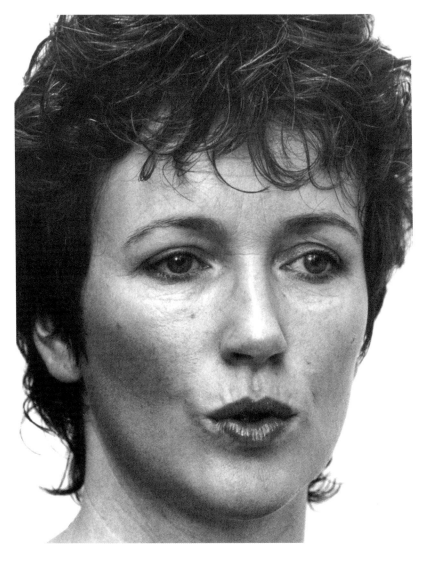

Who   **Food**   **Loop**

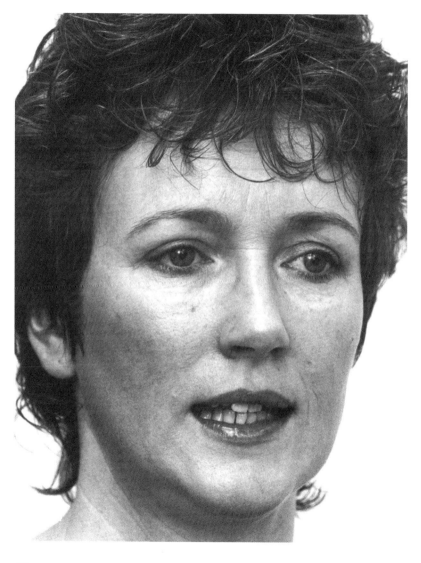

Easy   **Weak**   **Beech**

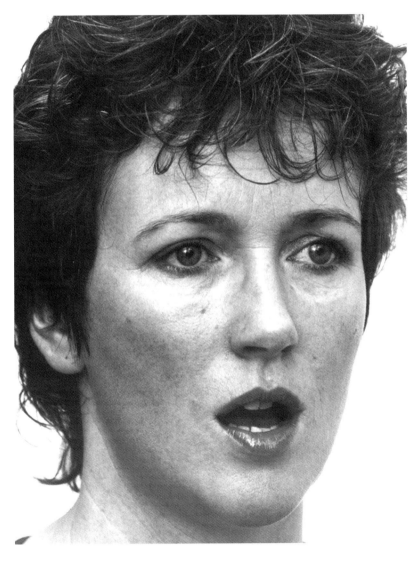

Bird **Early** **First**

Teachers using voiceless speech may use a whole session on each of the long vowels. Study the changes on your own image's face, as you go from one long vowel to another. Think of someone you have observed on the television who speaks practically without opening his lips, like a ventriloquist. Now try to say the long vowels AH, AW, OO, EE, ER, keeping your lips nearly closed. Remember to open your mouth when speaking clearly.

Some practice sentences for the mirror, or better still a friend who will read them, without voice, to you:

> **'Aren't her school fees awful?'**
>
> **'Articled clerks are taught by lawyers.'**
>
> **'He's a keen cheese eater.**
>
> **'He keeps geese to feed on the lawn.'**
>
> **'The early bird earns the worm.'**
>
> **'His car ought to do thirty-five mpg.'**
>
> **'Too much heat soon burns up food.'**
>
> **'Forty furtive fools feeding fast.'**
>
> **'You ought not to do that.'**

**'She's *always*
shopping in
Oxford Street.'
Stressing a word
in a sentence
changes meaning.**

Stress

Say the last sentence in the list on page 43 as you would to a child, quite quickly and then very carefully, as in the photographs. Think also of the rhythm of the sentence, and the accent on 'ought' and then on 'do', or possibly, the accent on 'not', and then on 'do'. This is all part of clear communication and lipreading.

Stress is especially important in English, since it changes the meaning. It is possible to take English sentences, eg "Would you like soup today?" and stress a different word five times, with five different meanings. It is possible to teach a good lipreader or a professional lipspeaker to look for this stress. More energy is put into the stressed syllable, and the vowel or consonant is elongated. Look at the difference between 'She's always shopping in Oxford Street', (not Bond Street, not Tottenham Court Road). 'She's always shopping in Oxford Street', (not just once a month or annually).

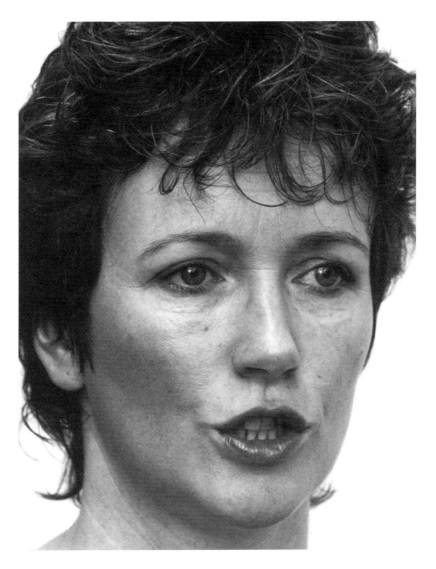

Surely   **Cautious**   **Blush**

Chapter 6

SH

Let's have a nice one to see next: SH. It is very visible and audible and often appears in speech. It is the sound you make when you put your finger in front of your mouth to mean 'hush'. Unfortunately, it is very much like some others – the soft CH ('chicken', 'urchin', 'machine'), J ('jeep'), and G ('George'). These are the main alternatives, but you get SH sounds in 'ocean', 'tension', 'session', 'caution', 'sure'. We sometimes notice in class that when speaking without voice it is difficult to say SH without making any sound; and the SH sound is one that a hearing aid may be boosting for those with a hearing loss in the high frequency sounds.

> **'Surely merchant ships should be cautious on the ocean. Their engines and machinery are subject to tensions.'**

> **'The urchin look makes a smashing fashion for teenagers.'**

> **'George took the picture.'**

TU is a borderline SH shape: 'mature', 'overture'. Some people make it a T shape, some a TCH. I think it looks like SH, even when pronounced T. Actually the sound in 'picture', 'mature' is CH which is a combination of T plus SH. This is why it resembles SH because the initial T is drowned by the bigger SH.

The 'sh' sound is easy to see and often appears in speech.

Of course, in spite of the spelling, 'Christians' are not admitted into this chapter, nor 'chorus girls'. They go with the gutteral K. Like the hard C, it is a sound made in the throat – very difficult to see, but easier to hear. 'Ginger', 'jackals' and 'Germans' are welcome, so are 'chickens' and 'cherries'.

See what happens when one shape ends a word and begins the next: 'George generally...', 'Cash shows...', 'Prime Minister...'. Words are what we have to see, and hear, so the more we know about them, and what people do to them as they speak, the better.

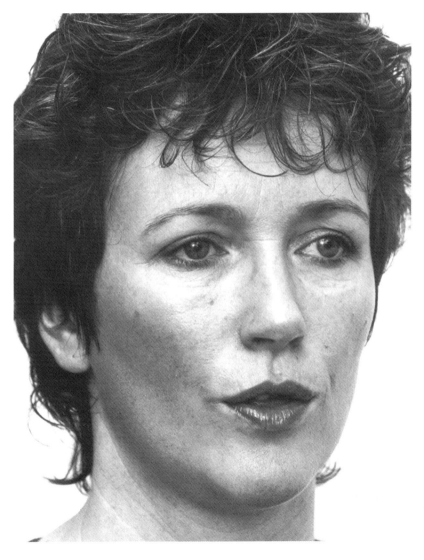

Think   **Rather**   **Bath**

Chapter 7

TH and the invisibles: T, D, N, hard G, hard C, hard K

Another consonant sound to follow SH. First study the photograph and how the sound is made. Get the feel of it, and note what you see in the mirror. People vary quite a lot. The shape is just the tip of the tongue peeping through between the teeth. Say to your mirror, 'I think this thing thoroughly disproves the theory.' It is easy to see TH when people part their lips as they speak, and sometimes it is visible from a side view of the speaker. The sound is not very easy to hear, but is a valuable signpost when seen. After the complications of the SH, J, and other sounds, TH has the great advantage that if TH is what you saw, then TH it is. Say 'the fifth thing' and see what happens. With most people the two THs will be seen as one, but just a tiny bit longer. Sometimes a person trying to be helpful may put the tongue right out, with the misguided idea that 'mouthing' words helps people who have a hearing loss.

The TH sound can only be made with the breath passing through the teeth with the tongue in the position illustrated. It is not a loud sound and missing teeth, or dentures, may affect it adversely. Lips not properly parted conceal the sight of the sound, and you may still need the help of mental alacrity, and guesswork as well.

T, D and N

Following the study of the TH sound, now is a good time to consider the sounds T, D and N which are made by the tongue just behind the top front teeth. Many who have had lessons in public speaking have been taught to make these sounds effectively. The words 'art' and 'and' are distinguished by making the T more explosive than the D. They are both made by forcing the breath between the tongue and the top front teeth, the 'd' being made audible less forcefully with voice. Compare the words 'candid' and 'tempted', and feel the difference. Spoken well, the Ts and Ds should be definitely audible, but are unlikely to be visible, so it is not possible to illustrate them with photographs.

N is also made with the tongue pressed up at the back of the top front teeth, but the breath is prevented from passing so it goes out through the nose with a nasal sound. (When the nasal passage is blocked by a common cold the 'd' sound results. The word 'nine' sounds like 'dide'.)

T and D are invisible to all intents and purposes for most of us. They give exercise to our guessing abilities. 'Tedious' is such a word. Speak it to your image in the mirror and see. Hard C and hard G and K are other examples of invisibles. Try 'cock', 'dog', 'cat', 'good', 'god' and 'tack'. Compare 'dog' and 'cat' and 'good' and see what difference there is.

I have often been puzzled by the word 'car'. It looks like 'ah'. Gradually I am learning that 'ah' is 'car'. I have also been stumped by 'dog' and 'doctor' more often than not. I shall never forget someone who came to the class occasionally. He was profoundly deaf. The teacher gave us each (without voice) one word to lipread. When she came to him she said 'dog'. He paused for a moment, then said, 'Well, it looks like a dog.' So when I call them invisibles, maybe they are not so to the expert.

Look out for the visible signs of speech to help you understand what is being said.

The one saving grace of the (to most of us) 'invisibles' is that they tend to be quite audible, so that when it is possible to use both hearing and lipreading together, one should get the message.

The words 'eight', 'nine' and 'ten' are difficult to distinguish by sight alone. Check by asking, 'Did you say nine?' If the answer is 'no', you must then ask again, 'Did you say eight?' If the answer is 'no' you will know the number must have been 'ten'.

Visible signs
Logical anticipation in the context, facial expression, small

gestures, all help the eyes to see the speech. Emphasis on a phrase, a word, or just a syllable, all play their part in making the meaning visible, provided nothing is allowed to distract the eyes from watching the face of the speaker.

Make sure that nothing distracts you from watching the speaker's face.

Whether or not you are in the habit of watching the newsreaders on TV, do keep reminding yourself to look out for the signposts of visible speech introduced so far – there are more to come. The human mind is perfectly capable of listening intelligently to a speaker and, at the same time, watching for the visible signs of speech. The difficulty is to remember to watch for them if, in the circumstances, you are hearing quite well.

Sound variations
Practise variations of the sounds in this and previous chapters with the following:

filth	**theft**
shift	**loft**
lathe	**lush**
thrill	**shun**
thatch	**lunch**

churlish   **church**

value   **vanish**

'Violence in films can be very frightening.'

'Fashion photography visually displays the latest fantasy.'

'Flowers in fragile vases frequently fail to survive.'

'A surfeit of fattening foods fails to improve the figure.'

'Verify the tension first.'

'Her favourite little vanities.'

'The verger's version failed to verify the facts.'

'Jellyfish.'

'George's journey over the ocean justified his ambition.'

The idea of this list is that you will study them on your image in the mirror, watching the formation of the signpost shapes as they happen. If you can then find someone to read out the whole list to you, without voice, you would get some real practice (and possibly some discouragement because it is a very difficult test). Ignoring the result of the voiceless exercise, repeat it with voice, because the whole aim is to enable the reader to combine seeing and hearing. It's the two together that works when, for most of us, we have awakened our eyes to see the sound.

L

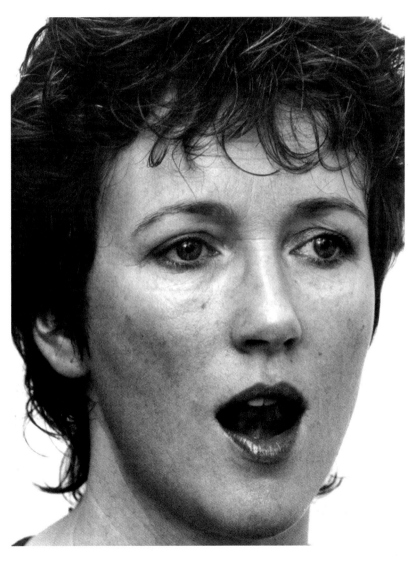

Lovely   **Syllable**   **Well**

Chapter 8

L and dark L

Start by saying into the mirror the sounds T, D, N, L a few times, and watch carefully. If you take it slowly, what you will see is that there is practically no difference between T and D, but there is something to see when you watch N and L; 'en' or 'and' compared with 'el'. Look at the photograph of L – the tip of the tongue travels upwards to touch the palate just behind the front top teeth. Spend a little time with the mirror saying 'el'.

The point I am making is that there is a very slight similarity between N and L. In the mirror, say 'when' and 'well' or 'When will William come?' Speak normally but fast, and then pedantically, showing the Ls. Say, 'When on earth will William come?' or, better still, see if you can induce someone else to say it to you. In the mirror say

little	**liable**
lovely	**liability**
lovable	**syllable**
apple	**you'll see**
apples	**people**

'People say silly things.'

These are a few samples, showing there are nice visible Ls and what have been called dark Ls which escape being seen, often part of a double consonant. As a signpost, L suffers from being vandalised by other sounds preceding or following it.

flat   **lance corporals**

flight   **feel the**

ambulance   **wealth**

black

When you are speaking, you may be unaware of the dark Ls, but you can always feel the L being made. This may seem all rather technical, but it is desirable so as to be able to tell your eyes what to look for. L is often seen if one gets a side view of the speaker. Some more Ls to watch:

blame   **glutton**

black   **plural**

flute   **slaughter**

It can be a matter of opinion whether an L is a dark, or visible. A speaker can certainly make them more visible by careful technique.

A sharp eye, an attentive ear, and an alert mind all add up to better hearing. L is not a loud sound, but it is audible: sometimes easy to see, but not always. Alertness (see this word in the mirror) of vision and mind is the key. Indeed, the word 'invisible' is not used by teachers of very good lipreaders because they always see something – either a face muscle moves, or the jaw, or a throat movement is seen. Of course it might be that their skill is now sufficient for them to be able to use their mental agility more quickly, and the teacher can never be sure what percentage of each is involved. If you have trouble with Ls, try this:

'Live and let live.'

'He who laughs loudest laughs last.'

Practise the 'L' shape in the mirror. 'He who laughs loudest laughs last.'

'Trouble' itself is a cause of difficulty with the L. A qualified lipspeaker can make the dark L more visible by just taking the trouble to do so. Say 'the trouble' and then 'the trouble to do so' in the mirror. In ordinary speech the L tends to get lost unless there is a momentary break between the '-ble' and the 't-' of '... to do so'. Try it in the mirror and decide whether to help the lipreader, or just talk and let him or her work it out. It rather depends on how good a lipreader you are speaking to. With a moment's effort you can let in a little light on a dark L. Another good example is 'wholemeal bread' compared with 'home-made bread'. Try both in the mirror. There is only a little difference. If you cannot see the dark Ls, only the long vowel EE is the clue.

59

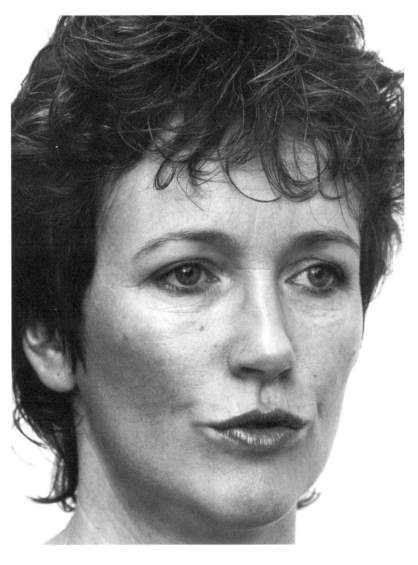

Rent   **Crane**   **Mirror**

Chapter 9

R and combinations

The shape photographed is the one most usually made. It is basically described as raising the inner side of the lower lip towards the upper teeth. There is movement of the chin upwards. It needs to be studied because there is a variation with different people. Of course, Scottish people roll their 'rrrs' with their tongue, but there is still something of the basic shape. It is a good shape to see. Compare it with the F in the mirror.

fat	**rat**	**rot**	**font**
fen	**rent**	**rook**	**foot**
fit	**writ**	**rut**	**fun**

There is a difference which you should be able to see. You also want to study what happens when the R is preceded by a 'b' or 'p' – 'brother', 'proud'. Repeat such words to the mirror without voice and also study what happens when other people say 'brother', 'bread', 'priest', 'friend', 'shred', 'thread'. Sometimes the 'b' of brother makes the shape change rather like a SH shape when the upper lip becomes involved. The curling of the lower lip is the characteristic of the R shape. Incidentally, 'mirror' is a good word to study. The M seems to affect the R.

For the mirror:

'Round the rugged rock the ragged rascal ran.'

When you say 'ran', watch and you will see the N at the end
as the tongue goes up while the lips are still open. 'Peter Pan'
gives another visible N if your tongue moves before your lips
and jaw close. Study 'pant' and 'pants'. So the 'n', 'nt', and
'nts' could be described as seeable and missable. Compare
'mother' and 'brother'.

Relax
Lipreading is a bit like playing darts. One day you are on
form and another day you miss a lot. The darts player usually
has a glass of beer at hand to keep his eye in. The lipreader
needs plenty of confidence to help out. The darts player gets
a bit of physical exercise, usually sitting comfortably. So the
lipreader's confidence is more likely to be nourished by a
relaxed mental attitude and a rest at intervals.

The R may be preceded by other consonants, for example
'b', 'p', 'sh', 'th', 't', 'f', 'g', 'c', 'k', 'd', or 'p'.

rain, train, grain, crane, drain

Unfortunately, it is difficult to see the difference. It is possible to hear the difference if your hearing is acute enough and there is always the context. When someone says 'rain', the context is likely to give the vital clue to the consonant which you have not seen. 'We'll be late for the train', 'We are short of grain for the chickens', 'We must have the drains seen to soon', 'Surely it can't go on raining much longer', 'We are overshadowed by that huge crane'.

Lipreading is like playing darts. One day you are on form, the next day you miss a lot.

When R or W end a word, they become part of the preceding vowel, and do not make any separate sound either visually or audibly. Examples: 'pillow', 'hollow', 'tomorrow', 'few', 'new', 'tar', 'war', 'poor', 'fur', 'for'. If the word ending with R or W is followed by a word beginning with the same sound – 'a new word' – or by a vowel – 'a rare art' – that's different. It all means you must watch out!

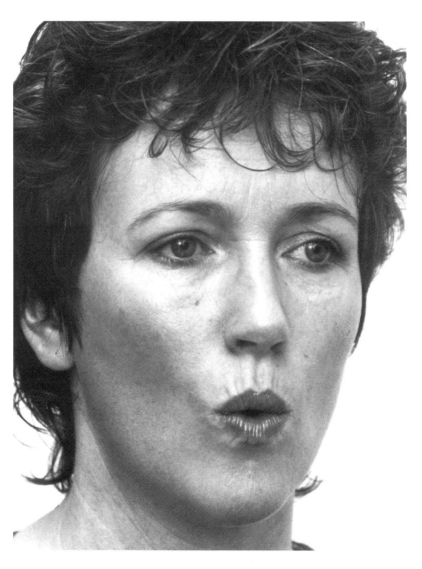

When   **One**   **Queen**

Chapter 10

W and Q

The W shape is rather, but not quite, like the OO vowel shape.
WH is visually almost the same as W.

'When do you want your breakfast?'

In English there is no W shape at the end of a word. In words
like 'pillow', 'chew', 'new' and 'draw', the W becomes part of
the vowel shape.

'A new word.'

'Waste not want not.'

'I don't owe you anything.'

A sentence beginning with a W may often be a question:
'What...?' 'Where...?' 'Which...?' 'When...?' 'Why...?' The
context and facial expression may be a clue.

Q and W have to be studied together. The difference between
them will seldom, if ever, be detectable by sight alone.
'Query' and 'weary' look exactly the same. 'Quite' and 'quick'
look like 'white' and 'wick'. 'Queen' looks like 'wean' and 'well'
may be 'quell'. 'Quandry' could be lipread as 'wandering' but
would not make sense. The W is rather nice and easy to see,
but I find it takes time to remember to become suspicious if
the W makes a word that doesn't fit the sentence. My
masterpiece of stupidity was once when royalty was the

subject, and I lipread the word 'wean' which did not make sense, and my mind searched for a W word which would. I quite forgot about the Queen!

You would be very lucky if you ever saw the difference between the KW which makes a Q and W. There may always be something which somebody can see: perhaps a faint delay before the W or a tiny movement in the throat.

'Write' and 'wrong' show that lipreading is only concerned with the phonetics or the actual sound, and not the spelling. It is quite possible that as one becomes more efficient at lipreading, the ability to spell correctly may deteriorate.

Finally, some more banana skins of which to beware:

quire – wire	**quake – wake**
quill – will	**quad – wad**
quest – west	**quip – whip**
quench – wench	**quirk – work**
quaver – waver	**quart – wart**
quarter – water	**query – weary**

I had a good example in the class of the advantages and disadvantages of the analytic and synthetic methods (see page 12), in relation to lipreading the Q/W shape. We had been reading, without voice, about a roof which needed various repairs. Then came a description of what happened when it rained and men had to come. The voiceless words were: 'They went up on the roof quickly and made a repair.' I must have been applying the mental anticipation of the synthetic method, because I lipread, inaccurately, that the men went up on the roof willingly (in the rain!). When you analyse my mistake, it was not important, but it was interesting how I got over the – to

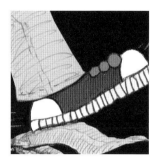

Lipreading is concerned with how a word sounds, not the actual spelling. Beware of slip-ups!

me – invisible Q. I found a suitable word beginning with W which did have two 'l's when 'quickly' has only one. Note that the most visible shapes were the W and the 'ly'. So I got 'wi' and 'ly' and I only cheated by putting two syllables where one had been spoken without voice. It could be said that I got the gist of the sentence.

Chapter 11

S, X and Z

There is no photograph of the S shape which is also the X, the Z shape and the soft C shape. This is because different people make quite a variety of shapes. Back to the mirror. See what shape you make for S.

'Sister Susie's sewing shirts for soldiers.'

'Sing a song of sixpence.'

Then try and observe what other people do. The ideal shape is when the upper and lower teeth are nearly closed and visible. But sometimes all there is to see is a slight movement in the corners of the mouth.

The X is really 'ecks' but the 'ck' comes among the not very visibles (see page 52). As a rule, X lipreads as S – 'extraordinary, 'excuse', 'exam'. Therefore a little caution should be attached to S. It may be X, like W may be Q. Sometimes S is pronounced Z, as in 'observe'. It is not always easy to see whether a word is singular or plural because the S gets lost at the end of the word. Also it can be difficult if there are too many S sounds, as in the word 'solicitors', or 'solicitous'. There is very little to see, even if the L is shown clearly, except a slight rapid movement of the jaw. With the help of context and practice, the word may become

lipreadable as a whole: "He had a legal problem and consulted his solicitor." Try it in the mirror, but never forget that you could ask a friend to come and speak to you without voice, and share the mirror.

Say 'Sing a song of sixpence'. See the slight movement of the S shape.

Chapter 12

Double vowels

The long vowels were illustrated in Chapter 5 – (AH, AW, OO, EE and ER). These cover a large number of vowel sounds with a variety of spellings. If you turn back to the chapter and remind yourself of what you saw in the mirror and the respective shapes, it will help now when we study what can be called the double vowels. They are OY as in 'boy' or 'oil', OW as in 'out' or 'cow', EAR as in 'ear', 'deer' and 'dear', and IE as in 'eye' or 'I' (the first person singular).

The important thing about these double vowels is that there is a sliding motion of the shapes as they move from one shape to the other. Now you need the mirror. The one I like best is 'boy'. Say it in the mirror.

> **'Come here, boy.'**
> **'Boys and girls.'**

It is almost impossible to cut the sliding movement, however sharply you say 'boy'. The vowel in 'boy' is a double one and the vowel in 'girl' is the long vowel ER.

Next the OW as in 'sound' or 'out': again you see the sliding shapes, even when speaking sharply: 'Out, damned spot.' Now 'ear': once more the sliding movement which makes it impossible to photograph EAR in a still photo. But you can see it

in speech and you can give it just that little help when speaking without voice.

Then there is IE:

'My eyesight improves with spectacles.'

'I deny fighting for my rights.'

'Come here, boy' has a double vowel where there is a sliding motion of the shape.

You can see the sliding movement in the mirror. Don't forget the possibility of studying these things on the lips of someone else if you can arrange it. OA as in 'owe' or 'home' or 'dole' or 'Oh, no don't' has got the sliding movement. Try it in the mirror. The great thing is to be able to recognise it in speech together with the context. It is a bit like the AW shape except for the 'o' closing towards the 'w' shape. Likewise there is the AY shape as in 'aim'. This is a sliding shape, as though there were a little 'I' after the basic 'a' shape. 'A', 'K', 'pay', 'cave', 'David', 'amazing', 'name', 'fade'.

For mirror practice say 'David' and 'darling' – that compares the AH single long vowel with the sliding AY shape.

More words to compare:

pavement	**pipework**
maintain	**martyr**
fool	**fated painter**
fade	**farmer**

You have to watch your image in the mirror carefully to see the slight difference. That is why lipreading needs a good deal of practice. So does your friend, if only to speak clearly without voice. It is possible to regard the OA shape as a long vowel plus a short vowel, 'Ooo' or 'owe', the 'oo' being the short vowel in 'good' and 'put'. In the same way, the AY shape could be 'AYI'.

Mirror practice for OA and AY: 'today', 'toad', 'dough', 'day', 'throw', 'hay', 'mow', 'may', 'moat', 'mate', 'most', 'Mayday', 'Pope', 'payday', 'date'.

The complete set of double vowels involving sliding motion is:

OY   **boy, oil, royal, foil, noise, ahoy, toy.**

EAR   **ear, hear, rear, sphere, mere, steer, career.**

OW   **out, flout, tout, sprout, count, mount.**

AIR   **air, care, where, share, hair, hare.**

AY   **day, say, they, eight, rate, mate.**

IE   **eye, my, sky, flight, might.**

OA   **owe, no, don't, moat, float, joke.**

EE/OO   ewe, new, due, few, huge, Hugh.

OOR   dour, lour.

The vowels of the alphabet appear again in the last four, and yet again in the next chapter on short vowels. It is useful to know about these things, but obviously you cannot analyse every vowel as you lipread, any more than you do when reading printed words. For the mirror:

'The aim of either boy is to throw it out.

'The heir to the throne travelled by air.'

pear	**pair**
pare	**mare**
fare	**bear** **(remember P, B, M?)**
bear	**bare**

It is useful to compare the words 'heart' and 'height', the long vowel AH with the double vowel I or IE. Try them in the mirror. You can say them with little difference, but you should show a slight widening of the lipshape with the sliding movement for 'height'. It is important for both lipreaders and speakers. The difference demands sharp observation by the lipreader, and careful speech.

The double vowel is really a mixture of two long vowels, long or short, or perhaps short and short.

Chapter 13

Short vowels, neutral vowels and accents

There is, of course, a vowel in every word. I have often thought that in the very first class one went to, or the very first time one saw a silent word on someone's lips, one recognised the vowel instinctively. It might have been a long vowel, a double vowel, or a short one. The complete concentration on someone's lips probably revives long-lost memories from our infancy and we are not actually surprised that we lipread the word or words. Lipreading, which is concerned with sounds, not spelling, has five long vowels, six short vowels and nine double vowels. Together with a neutral vowel, this makes 21 vowels in all. The five vowels of the alphabet represent 21 different sounds!

I like to divide short vowels into two sets of three. The first three are a bit difficult to distinguish from each other by sight. Back to the mirror again.

pat   pet   pit

Say them into the mirror. There is a little difference, but not much to see. The best thing to do with them is to class them as 'guessables' and move on to the next three.

pot   put   putt

Short vowels can be described as the offspring of the long ones and have a family resemblance.

These are more visible. Study them carefully in the mirror. It is interesting – they happen to be a, e, i, o and two u's!

The short vowels often occur in speech. I have seen them described as the little offspring of the long ones, or something like that. There is some truth in it. Try making a comparison in the mirror. Say 'pot' and then 'port', or try 'put' and 'port'. Compare 'put' and 'pert'. Remind yourself of the long vowels AW and ER. Try 'put' and 'who' (long vowel OO). Then 'hood' and 'who'. It does not matter whether you see a family resemblance in the shapes, as long as you get the idea. It is all helping the eyes to see sounds rapidly, as they do when reading the printed word. Thinking back, one has been lipreading short vowels without knowing it, in the course of studying the long ones, and the consonants. Some short vowels crop up in almost anything you say. Again it makes me wonder whether we have all noticed much more about the visible appearance of speech than we consciously realise.

Studying words with the sounds of the short vowels is helpful, and I have found it useful to commit to memory the six similar words containing the six short vowels.

a	e	i	o	u	u
pat	pet	pit	pot	put	putt
at	end	it	hot	good	under
sad	said	is	dog	should	undo
thank	dead	isn't it	cough	could	jungle
mad	head	ink	trough	wood	rough

For those who have some hearing, with or without a hearing aid, the 'pat', 'pet', 'pit' ones are easy to hear and not so easy to see, but the 'pot', 'put' and 'putt' ones are easy to hear and a bit easier to see.

Previously (page 12) I have referred to the analytic method of lipreading when we have a single word to see, without context or clue. Then the mind has to break down the word into consonant and vowel (long or short). This would be appropriate with short vowels when you have seen the shape of, say, either 'hot', 'hood' or 'hut' and recognised it. The word 'dog' has the short vowel 'o', like 'hot'. Watch your image saying 'hot dog'. There is a difference to see but it is pretty difficult. So with 'good' or 'gut', especially without context or clue. The analytical recognition of these vowels might help with a context, but if the short vowel is not recognised and there is no context, there is, lipreading-wise, almost no word. So the best thing to do is to ignore it and go to the next and

A practised lipreader usually knows if someone has an accent.

the next, in the hope that something will give a clue. This is the synthetic or rhythmic method.

Neutral vowels are found in: 'mother', 'father', 'sister', 'banana', 'enemy'. A whole word may become neutral depending on stress, for example: 'cup of tea', 'bunch of flowers'. So the neutral vowel plays a very important part in our language – it gives us rhythm. In French, for example, all vowels carry equal weight. Watch as you say 'bunch of flowers' giving each word equal stress. Now say it naturally – can you see the difference?

Effect of accents on vowels

With all vowels, accent affects the shape. Remember the old song: 'You say tomatoes and I say tomatoes'? (tom ah toes/toe may toes). Another example – someone with a Northern accent may pronounce the word 'bath' with a short vowel 'a', where a Southerner may say 'bath' with the long 'ah'. When coming across someone with an accent for the first time, it can throw you but, once you realise they have an accent, you can readily 'tune' in to it and you will soon be lipreading in that accent. When you become a practised lipreader you will begin to tell after a while that someone is talking to you with an accent. One of the great advantages of being a lipreader (and there are many) is that you may well be able to tell where someone comes from just by watching them speak.

Chapter 14

Speaking without voice

You need to be relaxed to speak clearly without using your voice. It is a strain if the lipreader cannot read you, but you must keep calm and never try to 'mouth' in an attempt to help. Only the slightest exaggeration is readable. Keep the rhythm, slow down a little, repeat a few times. Then, if necessary, stop and speak with voice, or write it down. Whenever you speak, remember that someone listening may not hear too well. Even unaffected ears will hear all the better if you speak with voice. Always be careful not to damage the lipreader's confidence. If she or he has not understood after a few attempts, write it down.

Some other rather obvious rules:

- Get the attention of the person who will be lipreading.

- Look at the person before you start.

- When you begin, remember to feel your lips working and your mouth moving. But don't 'mouth' words, don't exaggerate more than a trifle but pronounce every syllable.

- Don't fidget, don't move your head about, or wave your arms or put your hand in front of your mouth.

- Don't smile because it will change the shapes. See that your face is in good light.

One day in class, the teacher asked each of us a question without voice. Not thinking, I answered without voice. There was an embarrassing moment for both of us until I repeated my reply out loud. That started me seriously to think whether my voiceless talk was lipreadable. Indeed, I am still thinking. It is one thing to see your image in the mirror making all the right shapes, and another to remember to feel yourself making the shapes clearly when speaking to someone.

It is good training to think what you are saying, and feel yourself making the lipshapes as you speak. Talking to other lipreading students, there are several things to be conscious of at the same time: Are they hearing you? Are they good at lipreading? Could you phrase it better? Are you speaking clearly without voice? It is very easy to lipread your image in the mirror because you know what it is saying. Only trial and error will tell you whether you are doing it properly, and that it is easily lipreadable to other people. Anyone who has made a serious attempt to master the lipshapes illustrated should be easier to lipread than most hearing people talking colloquially.

An example might be the word 'curtain'. Most people would say it as one syllable – 'curtn'. Say it to your image in the mirror and feel how you make the 'tn' sound – the tongue comes up behind the front teeth closing the mouth (not the lips) and air is blown down the nose from the back. Now say the word 'curt' and note the difference. Now say the word 'colonel' or 'kernel', followed by 'earn' or 'urn'. The 'n' is the nasal one. In 'turn', the 't' actually needs some outgoing breath. So to say the word correctly, as distinct from the way you might normally, 'curtain' is two syllables – 'cur t-n'. Say one after the other 'curn', 'curt', 'cur t-n', 'kernel', 'urn', 'turn'. Note what you can see and what you can hear. 'The colonel asked him to draw the curtains, turn on the light and earn his thanks.' Note how helpful a bit of context can be.

People who speak through their teeth, like ventriloquists, are very difficult to lipread.

Rephrase

Speaking without voice also requires mental agility. If you can see that what you say is not being lipread, the thing to do is to rephrase it, using the words with easy lipshapes if you can think of some quickly. A phrase with a number of words, or a sentence, spoken at even a normal speed, leaves a lipreader little time to operate with mental agility in return. A basic skill in speaking without voice is to slow down enough to help the lipreader's problems, without losing the rhythm of a sentence. The human mind tends to anticipate that a conversation will

Always get the attention of the lipreader before you start speaking.

run upon the same lines unless warned of a change. For instance, if the subject has been domestic chores and you suddenly change it by asking, 'Do you like watching sport?' you may get a good laugh if your lipreader replies, 'No, I don't like washing smalls.' There's very little difference between 'sport' and 'smalls'. Try them in the mirror.

When you speak to a lipreader always make sure that the first few words, indicating the general subject, have been understood, particularly if you are speaking without voice.

'Ventriloquists'

Lipreaders have to work hard trying to read all the 'ventriloquists' they meet in daily life, so deserve a little help when you know how to speak without voice. Never overdo it. In spite of all temptations, keep the rhythm, speak a bit slower and clearer. Whenever you have a good view of the speaker's face, the television is a good source for practice for lipreading and speaking clearly without voice. Take one of the illustrated shapes and watch for it. You can do this as well as following the programme.

Notice those speakers who show clear shapes, have mobile lips, and speak so well that you can listen to every word and lipread quite a lot. Notice the ones who speak through their teeth with little movement and then, of course, the 'ventriloquists' who rarely part their lips at all. It is always good practice to listen to the meaning of what is being said and watching what it looks like at the same time. The day may come when, reading voiceless speech successfully, you get an uncanny feeling as though you had heard it.

Chapter 15

Final thoughts

Through the Looking Glass (with apologies to Lewis Carroll):
"'How can I hear you if you don't speak up?' roared the
Queen at Alice. 'She should hear what she can and see what
she can't,' said the Cheshire Cat and promptly vanished.'"

It takes a cat to sum it all up in so few words. So let us look
back into the looking glass.

It takes time to acquire a habit, good or bad. The good habit
you must get is to look whenever you listen. The brain can
cope easily with seeing and listening together. I will never
forget seeing a church organist playing the music with his
hands and feet, pushing and pulling the stops while he
carried on a conversation with someone behind him. We can
concentrate on both the sound and sight of speech, get the
meaning and agree or disagree with it, all at once. The 12
lipshapes illustrated are the easiest to see and recognise as
they form momentarily during speech and must be learned.

As children we all went through it to learn the alphabet and then
to read. With practice, we learned to see groups of letters as
words at a glance, even long words, or several words. First we
had to know the letters. The printed word stays put on the
paper. The lipshaped words are in constant movement, together

**Don't opt out!
There is a wealth
of technical
equipment which
can make your
life easier.**

with the sound. The advantage we have over the child is that we already know the language. Very few, if any, of us have never noticed something of what speech looks like.

Go back to the 12 shapes, one at a time, and see if you can concentrate on each whenever you see anyone speaking. A good way to get practice is with the television when you can see the speaker's face well. Reduce the volume of sound to a point when you can only just hear it. Alternatively, turn off your hearing aid. I think, under such conditions, the memory of lipshapes learned is stimulated and sight begins to assist the sound. The P, B and M shape (lips closed) becomes more noticeable. The F and V shape seems easier to see and the same with the SH and various others, even with rapid speech.

You will be your own taskmaster. If you find both master and pupil are none too diligent, don't give up too soon. Remember the mirror. Here is one to think about. The long vowel OO and the consonant W (QU): the photographs do show the difference – just. Practise them in the mirror. 'Two hooligans went away.' 'What do you want?' 'The wet winter was quite wonderful for the flowers.' 'Who has won?' 'One, two'.

From now on you have to invent your own exercises and lipreading problems. See if you can remember the five long vowels and seven consonant shapes. Every time you think about them, see them on your reflection's face or other people's, and you are one degree nearer the day when you cannot quite hear until you can see the speakers. It is a great day. Remember you learn more from other people's lips than from your own. Still more from attending a class with a qualified teacher, where you will meet others like yourself, even some who are profoundly deaf.

One last thought: any loss of hearing can contribute to turning a human being into a 'loner' who opts out. All the time things are happening to help us to opt in, such as loop systems, textphones, flashing doorbells and vibrating alarm clocks, and subtitled programmes make television more relaxing. More and more hearing people are learning about what hard of hearing people need to make life easier: the scientists are working all the time to improve our lot. Watch out for all these things.

Appendix 1

Lipspeaking

What is a lipspeaker?

A qualified lipspeaker works with deaf and hard of hearing people who rely on lipreading and speech to communicate. Without using their voice, the lipspeaker repeats what a hearing person or speaker says and you lipread what has been said. A lipspeaker does this by producing clearly the shape of words, the flow, rhythm and phrasing of natural speech, and by repeating the stress as used by the speaker. The lipspeaker also uses facial expression, natural gesture and fingerspelling (if requested) to help you understand what has been said.

Speech that is too fast for lipreading may have to be cut down by the lipspeaker, who is not more than a sentence behind the speaker. Many people speak up to 200 words a minute, so lipspeaking involves great concentration. If two speakers are talking at the same time, neither message can be passed on. Lipspeakers are also trained to give a voiced transmission of the lipreader's message if asked to do so. Lipreaders usually have a good level of English.

Who uses lipspeakers?

Lipspeakers are used by deaf, deafened and hard of hearing people whose main method of communication with other people is lipreading and speech. A hearing person may also use a lipspeaker to communicate with deaf people.

How can a lipspeaker help you?

A lipspeaker can help in a range of different situations, for example:

Adult education

Further and higher education

Conferences and meetings

Training courses

Job interviews

Hospital appointments

Legal work

Religious services

Political open meetings

There are two levels of lipspeaking: Level 2 and Level 3, each with a different level of expertise. When looking for a lipspeaker, you need to think about the type of meeting or situation in which you will be asking them to lipspeak.

All lipspeakers are expected to conform to a professional Code of Practice and must keep all information on assignments strictly confidential.

Who pays?

You can usually get financial support to pay for a lipspeaker at work through the Government's Access to Work (ATW) scheme. If you are unemployed, contact your local Jobcentre, which will refer you to the Disability Employment Adviser (DEA). The DEA will assess whether you are

Trained lipspeakers aid communication between hearing people and lipreaders.

eligible to apply for ATW. If you are working, arrange to meet your DEA. When you have been accepted for ATW, you and your employer can arrange for your support.

If you need a lipspeaker for an appointment with your doctor or at a hospital, let them know in plenty of time. The doctor or hospital may have a budget to pay for communication support in such cases, in line with the requirements of the Disability Discrimination Act. Your social services may also be able to help. If you need communication support in court, paying for this is not your responsibility, except in some civil law situations.

Further information

For further information on lipspeaking contact RNID or the
Association of Lipspeakers (see Useful addresses on page 103).

Appendix 2

Hearing aids

If you think you have a hearing loss you should visit your GP (family doctor). He or she will probably send you to a hospital for a hearing test. If the results show that a hearing aid will help you, an impression of your ear will be taken and you will be fitted with a hearing aid. It takes a bit of time getting used to a hearing aid – putting it in, taking it out, working the volume control and getting used to the sound. If you do not get on well with the hearing aid, go back to the hearing aid centre. Remember that if you only have an aid in one ear, you have some loss of ability to judge the direction from which sound is coming and you must use your eyes even more in traffic.

The hearing aid I have has a switch marked O-T-M. When the switch is in the 'O' position the hearing aid is OFF, in the 'T' position I am able to use the TELECOIL function (for using a loop system), and 'M' is for general use, ie MICROPHONE. There is also a compartment for the battery and a small wheel. If you turn the little wheel one way, it increases the volume of sound and the other way reduces the sound. You will find it a great help to learn which way is which when you have the aid in place behind your ear. Different volumes may suit you better in different listening conditions – having a conversation, listening to the TV or radio, or when there is background noise.

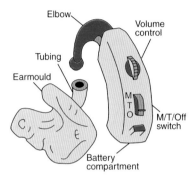

A hearing aid setting that is best for following speech does not work so well with music. However, some advanced hearing aids now have alternative settings for different listening situations.

Ear wax

It is natural for ear wax to be produced in the canal in the outer ear (from outside to the eardrum). Sometimes wax may be produced or collect in excess. Your doctor may prescribe drops which you put into the ear canal for a few days to soften the wax, and you may then need to have the ear canal syringed to remove the wax. Normally this is quite effective and harmless. Never put anything in your ears thinking you can solve the problem yourself as you can cause damage to your ears. Always seek medical advice.

Further information

For more information see the RNID leaflets, *Look after your ears*, *All about hearing aids* and *Ears and ear problems*.

Appendix 3

Loops and infrared systems

Many of the difficulties that hard of hearing people have hearing in auditoria such as theatres or churches are due to the blurring effects of room acoustics. The problem is made worse by the distance that sound travels to the audience. Background noise and competing sounds are also a nuisance. There are two systems that help to get around these problems: audio frequency induction loops ('loops') and infrared systems.

Loop systems

Loops let you listen to your television, radio or stereo without being connected to it by a wire. You need a hearing aid with a 'T' position on the switch to use a loop. If you do not have a hearing aid, you can use a loop with a device called a loop listener instead.

A loop consists of a coil of wire run around the edge of a room. The ends of the wire are connected to a loop amplifier, which is attached to the equipment you want to listen to, either directly or using a microphone. The amplifier receives the sound signal, which is converted into magnetic waves by the loop. When these waves reach your hearing aid or loop listener, they are converted back into sound which you can hear.

Loops cut out background noise and room acoustics, so you hear only the sound you want to hear, and it is clearer. They come in different sizes. You may have seen signs in theatres or cinemas saying that a loop is installed. A loop in your home would be smaller. If you want a loop at home, social services should be able to provide one free of charge.

You might prefer a personal loop system. These use neckloops or earloops plugged into the equipment you want to listen to. The television or other equipment you are listening to must have a SCART socket.

Infrared systems

You may also have seen infrared systems in public places such as theatres. An infrared system consists of a transmitter and a receiver. The transmitter takes its signal from the sound source – the television or radio – either through a plug and socket, or through a microphone. It then converts the sound into invisible infrared light. Like loops, infrared systems let you move around the room freely. You are not attached to the equipment you are listening to by wires, you simply wear a small receiver.

The receiver that you wear picks up the infrared light and converts it back into sound. There are two different kinds of receiver – one for people who wear hearing aids and one for people who do not.

Strong sunlight interferes with infrared systems, so a very sunny room may not be a suitable place to have one installed.

Where can loops or infrared be used?

Hard of hearing people may find induction loops and infrared systems useful anywhere they need to hear a particular source of sound. They can be used in theatres, cinemas, churches, meeting rooms, conference halls and lecture rooms, and for announcements in airports, shopping centres, or stations.

Counter loops are useful for bank or ticket office windows where there is a glass screen between staff and customers. The glass should be non-reflective so that a deaf or hard of hearing customer can lipread. Infrared systems are more limited in their range of uses because listeners need a special receiver.

For further information on loops and infrared systems, see Induction loop and *infrared systems – a guide for deaf and hard of hearing people* (factsheet), *Sound and subtitles – making the most of audiovisual equipment* (leaflet), and the *Solutions* catalogue, all available from the RNID Information Line (see Useful addresses on page 103).

Publications

RNID Leaflets

All about hearing aids

Benefits and services for deaf and hard of hearing people

Communication services for deaf and hard of hearing people

Ears and ear problems

Equipment for deaf and hard of hearing people

Lipreading and lipspeaking

Look after your ears

Losing your hearing as you get older

Sound and subtitles – making the most of audiovisual equipment

RNID factsheets

Digital hearing aids

Doorbells – information for deaf and hard of hearing people

Induction loop and infrared systems – a guide for deaf and hard of hearing people

Listening equipment to help you in everyday situations

Multi-alerting systems to let you know about different sounds in your home

The NHS hearing aid service

Subtitles on television, DVD and video tapes

Telephones – information for deaf and hard of hearing people

A wide range of products for deaf and hard of hearing people can also be found on the RNID Shop and Equipment Database on the RNID website **www.rnid.org.uk**

Videos

How to overcome hearing loss: Desmond Wilcox explains how hearing aid users can cope in a range of situations such as noisy places and restaurants.

Introduction to lipreading: Lipreading teacher Patricia Sherren explains how to lipread more quickly and more easily than ever before.

Both videos are available from
Lipservice, Milton House, Stratfield Saye RG7 2BT.
Telephone 01256 882740 or 01306 882449.
Price: £19 each or two for £30.

Useful addresses

Association of Lipspeakers (ALS)
5 Furlong Close, Upper Tean, Stoke-on-Trent ST10 4LB
Telephone 01538 722482
Textphone 01538 722442
enquires@lipspeaking.co.uk www.lipspeaking.co.uk

Association of Teachers of Lipreading to Adults (ATLA)
PO Box 506, Hanley, Stoke-on-Trent ST2 9RE
ATLA@lipreading.org.uk www.lipreading.org.uk

City Lit Centre for Deaf People
41 Tavistock Square, London WC1H 9EX
Telephone 020 7383 7624
Textphone 020 7380 0416 Fax 020 7380 1076

Hearing Concern
7-11 Armstrong Road, London W3 7JL
Telephone 020 8743 1110
Textphone 020 8742 9151 Fax 020 8742 9043
Helpdesk 0845 074 4600 (voice/textphone)
info@hearingconcern.org.uk www.hearingconcern.org.uk

Link Centre for Deafened People

19 Hartfield Road, Eastbourne, East Sussex BN21 2AR
Telephone 01323 638230
Textphone 01323 739998 Fax 01323 642968
linkcntr@dircon.co.uk www.linkcentre.org

National Association of Deafened People (NADP)

PO Box 50, Amersham, Buckinghamshire HP6 6XB
Telephone/Textphone 01494 723613
Fax 01494 431932

RNID Tinnitus Helpline

19-23 Featherstone Street, London EC1Y 8SL
Tinnitus Helpline 0808 808 6666 (voice)
Textphone 0808 808 0007   Fax 020 7296 8199
tinnitushelpline@rnid.org.uk www.rnid.org.uk

RNID Information Line

19-23 Featherstone Street London EC1Y 8SL
Telephone 0808 808 0123
Textphone 0808 808 9000 Fax 020 7296 8199
informationline@rnid.org.uk www.rnid.org.uk

About RNID and ATLA

RNID

RNID is the largest charity representing the 9 million deaf and hard of hearing people in the UK. As a membership charity, we aim to achieve a radically better quality of life for deaf and hard of hearing people. We do this in the following ways:

- Campaigning and lobbying to change laws and government policies.

- Providing information and raising awareness of deafness, hearing loss and tinnitus.

- Training courses and consultancy on deafness and disability.

- Communication services including sign language interpreters.

- Training of interpreters, lipspeakers and speech-to-text operators.

- Seeking lasting change in education for deaf children and young people.

- Employment programmes to help deaf people into work.

- Care services for deaf and hard of hearing people with additional needs.

- Typetalk, the national telephone relay service for deaf and hard of hearing people.

- Equipment and products for deaf and hard of hearing people.

- Social, medical and technical research.

ATLA

The Association of Teachers of Lipreading to Adults (ATLA) is the only professional association for trained lipreading teachers. ATLA holds lists of lipreading teachers and their classes across the country. ATLA aims to:

- Provide a professional and recognised association for qualified teachers of lipreading to adults.

- Maintain and develop standards of lipreading teaching to adults.

- Promote understanding of the needs of people with an acquired hearing loss, whether partial or total.

- Advance the awareness of the benefits of lipreading and other communication skills in the rehabilitation of people with an acquired hearing loss.

- To coordinate and disseminate up-to-date information on all aspects of acquired deafness and on teaching methods and materials for members of the association.

- Provide support for qualified lipreading teachers enabling them to serve the needs of hearing impaired people.